THE ULTIMAT

Activity Coordinator Handbook

By Successful Care Home Activities

The Ultimate Activity Coordinator Handbook

Introduction

The Ultimate Activity Coordinator Handbook is a valuable resource for those working in elderly care homes. It has been written by an experienced activity coordinator who has worked in the UK's care homes for over ten years. The handbook contains a set of processes that will help you deliver meaningful and person-centred activities in your care setting.

In addition to tips and resources, the handbook will help reduce staff workload, which is especially useful for those of you working alone or in small teams with limited budgets. We suggest taking the time to read through the handbook first and getting familiar with the goals you are trying to achieve. So, grab a cup of tea, sit down, and enjoy learning about how to engage your residents in meaningful activities.

With this handbook, you'll have all the tools you need to build successful relationships with them.

When you're ready to begin, complete each task in chronological order to ensure that you don't miss any important steps.

So, good luck… and happy activity planning!

THE IMPORTANCE OF ACTIVITY PROVISION IN AN ELDERLY CARE HOME

- INCREASES MOBILITY
- STIMULATES BRAIN ACTIVITY
- HEIGHTENS FEELINGS OF EMOTIONAL WELLBEING
- CONNECTS RESIDENTS WITH FUN HOBBIES AND PASTIMES
- GIVES A FEELING OF EMPOWERMENT AND SELF-PRIDE
- GIVES EXTERNAL STIMULATION AND FRESH AIR
- RECONNECTS RESIDENTS TO FAMILY

To illustrate the above points, complete the following task.

What are the positive physical and emotional feelings that you experience when doing fun activities?
List 5 of them below:

1. ....

2. ....

3. ....

4. ....

5. ....

The above question was just a simple task to get you thinking about the feelings that your residents might want to experience when they take part in an activity.

The tasks presented in this handbook are intended to be completed during your workday, and with the involvement of the residents. They are designed to provide you with the necessary information to deliver activities that are wanted, as well as needed, by the residents.

Please follow the tasks in the order they appear in the handbook.

SECTION 1

Planning Person-Centred Activities

 TASK 1: GETTING TO KNOW THE RESIDENTS

To successfully get to know your residents, it's important to gather background facts.

TASK 1: Complete an individual **Me and My Life** form with each resident, to help you become familiar with their interests, backgrounds, needs, and emotional triggers.

Complete this task within the next two weeks if possible, as these forms will equip you with the information you need to keep each resident happy.

If a resident declines to participate, that's okay. Try approaching them again in a few weeks' time as they may feel differently then.

Keep this information in their files and refer to it regularly i.e. don't forget those key dates that they told you about. The care staff and kitchen should be made aware of any relevant information too. A Me and My Life form should be completed as standard for each new resident that enters the home.

These records will not only help the existing team, but they will also be useful to new members of staff, especially if a resident goes on to develop dementia and cannot communicate their needs well. If a current resident has already been diagnosed with dementia, it may be necessary to ask a family member or friend to fill in the gaps.

 On the next page, you will find a full-size A4 copy of the **Me and My Life form.** Photocopy one for each resident - or use the design as a template to create a more suitable one of your own!

Once you have a completed set of forms, you can move onto **Task 2 – Understanding the needs of the residents.**

ME AND MY LIFE

THE IMPORTANT THINGS THAT I WANT THE STAFF TO KNOW ABOUT ME

NAME:

DATE OF BIRTH	
WHERE I GREW UP	
MY PARENT'S NAMES AND OCCUPATIONS	
WHERE I LIVED BEFORE I MOVED IN HERE	
MY HUSBAND'S/WIFE'S NAME	
MY WEDDING ANNIVERSARY DATE	
WHERE I USED TO WORK	
WHERE MY HUSBAND / WIFE USED TO WORK	
MY CHILDREN'S NAMES AND BIRTHDAYS	
THE CLOTHES /JEWELLERY I PREFER TO WEAR INDOORS	
THE CLOTHES / JEWELLERY I PREFER WHEN GOING OUT	
COLOUR/ STYLE OF CLOTHES I DON'T LIKE	

MY FAVOURITE PASTIMES AND ENTERTAINMENT / FAVOURITE FILMS / MUSIC / BOOKS etc.	
DATES THAT I FEEL SAD How I would like the staff to help me on those days.	
THINGS THAT WORRY ME ABOUT MOVING INTO A RESIDENTIAL HOME	
THINGS THAT I AM LOOKING FORWARD TO DOING WHILE I AM HERE.	
MY FAVOURITE EDIBLE TREATS	
PETS THAT I WOULD LIKE TO REMEMBER	
CONVERSATION SUBJECTS THAT I ENJOY	
THINGS THAT MIGHT UPSET/ ANNOY ME IF I WERE TO EXPERIENCE THEM IN THE RESIDENTIAL HOME	
THINGS THAT WOULD HELP ME TO FEEL SETTLED HERE	

TASK 2: UNDERSTANDING THE INDIVIDUAL NEEDS OF RESIDENTS

Part A of this task should only take about 15 minutes, but it will help you to understand what many residents in the home might be feeling, daily. Most have lost loved ones over the years, and they have probably now lost a lot of their independence.

How might they be feeling? The following task will help you to understand these feelings on a deeper level.

 TASK 2 – PART A

Take a few moments to think about what you are truly grateful for in your life. This might include material possessions, loved ones, or enjoyable days out.

Here are some examples to get you started. I am grateful for:

1. Being able to walk down the street without help.
2. Being free to go out and buy a coffee.
3. Having pets in my life.
4. Feeling safe.
5. Having my family and friends nearby.
6. Being able to buy and read books.
7. Being able to watch the birds in the garden.
8. Being able to volunteer at the local castle.
9. Being able to work and earn my own money.
10. Good health.

Now it's your turn. List 10 things that you are truly grateful for in *your* life:

1...

2...

3...

4...

5...

6...

7...

8...

9...

10...

TASK 2 – PART B

Now consider some of the residents in your care setting. What might they have once valued and <u>lost</u> due to old age / declining health / moving into a care home?

These losses could include eyesight, hobbies, days out, parents, careers, mobility, pets, family, friends, personal items, or their home.

They may also miss just being asked for their opinion on things.

List 10 of those things below:

1...

2...

3...

4...

5...

6...

7...

8...

9...

10...

You should now have a clearer vision of what your residents miss in their lives.
Time to move onto **Task 3 – understanding the emotional impact of this loss.**

TASK 3: UNDERSTANDING THE EMOTIONAL IMPACT OF LOSS

TASK 3 is a tool designed to help care home staff understand the needs of specific residents who may be hard to engage with.

a) Take the 10 losses that you identified in the previous task (Task 2-Part B) and list them in column 1 of the table below.

b) In column 2, write down the emotions that a person might be feeling as a result of that loss.

E.g. the loss of freedom to walk to a favourite café whenever they want, might lead to feelings of frustration, sadness, or boredom. Or, the loss of meaningful hobbies might lead to feelings of helplessness, or resentment.

	COLUMN 1 Things that your residents once valued but have now lost	COLUMN 2 What emotion might your resident be feeling, having lost that person/thing/ability listed in Column 1?
1		
2		
3		
4		
5		
6		
7		
8		
9		
10		

It is important to be mindful of these emotions when planning activities for the residents.

Take another moment to consider the above losses and emotions before moving onto **Task 4 – Getting better acquainted with the residents.**

TASK 4: GETTING BETTER ACQUAINTED WITH EACH RESIDENT

As a staff member in an elderly care home, it is crucial to have good conversational skills. Through conversation you can get better acquainted with the residents and discover their unique needs. While not everyone is a natural conversationalist, anyone can acquire these skills with simple tools and practice. These communication tools are also useful in maintaining healthy relationships in all walks of life.

The purpose of TASK 4 is to develop your conversation skills and enable you to provide more measured mental health care to each resident through your social interaction and activities. As a result, you will be able to create an environment where residents and staff look forward to spending time with you.

If you struggle to converse with certain people, try the following **3-STEP RULE**:

Identify a resident that you don't know how to start a conversation with - maybe someone who is a bit quieter and more withdrawn than the others.

 STEP 1: Approach them in a casual way with the opening line:

"Hello, I'm just passing. How are you?"

(Tip: Avoid asking them if they want some company if they usually say no. Just stick with the above line of dialogue.)

 STEP 2: Advance the conversation by making a comment about something general that they can <u>easily</u> engage with, and follow with a simple question, e.g.

"The roads are busy today. Was it always this bad?"

Or: *"I've been looking at some pictures of... (fill in the blank with a local holiday destination)* **Have you ever been there"?**

 STEP 3: If they respond with a simple, *'yes'* or *'no'* keep the conversation going for just a few moments more by saying something like,

"What were the roads like where you lived then?" or *"Where did you used to go on holiday?"*

> **IMPORTANT: To keep a conversation going, it is important that you are genuinely interested in what the other person is telling you, (or at least act like you are) and that you ask lots of questions. This is a great opportunity to find out more about what each resident is interested in. By spending more time listening than talking, you will make that person feel valued, and that their thoughts and experiences matter to you.**

You can use the **3-step 'conversation starter' rule** to start a dialogue with anyone in any setting.

TASK 4: Now, practice using the 3-STEP RULE to get to know each of the residents a little better. You will enjoy getting them to open up about all sorts of things e.g. hobbies, where they used to live, the things that they loved doing - almost anything you can think of.

This technique is a good way to start group conversations too.

TIP: With two-way dialogue, try to avoid asking questions that allow someone to just answer 'yes,' or 'no,' as that can kill conversation very quickly.

Instead, ask 'prompting' questions such as:

I'll bet that was lovely, wasn't it?

Did you enjoy that? Please tell me more!

What else do you know about this area?

What was it like there?

I bet it was fun being a teenager back then, wasn't it?

I can imagine that it was a hard/fun job, wasn't it?

WHY USE PROMPTING QUESTIONS?

Using conversational prompts will keep the dialogue flowing in a mentally stimulating and positive direction.

Encourage residents to focus on positive memories - but do acknowledge when they need to talk about more emotional feelings. This will improve their mental wellbeing and they will value you as a person that they like and trust. As a result, the residents will be more likely to participate in the activity sessions that you offer.

Time to move on to **Task 5 – Creating person-centred activity plans.**

TASK 5: CREATING PERSON-CENTRED ACTIVITY PLANS

Being an activity coordinator is not an easy job. It can be exhausting and demotivating trying to navigate your way through so many daily challenges, while managing the expectations of the residents, their families, and the various care home staff.
But now we get to the part of the handbook that helps you to streamline your activity plan and lessen your workload. Things are about to get much better!

Hopefully, the conversations in Task 4 broke the ice with the residents, and that you got to know each other a little better.

TASK 5 involves you now working even more closely with each of them to create their **Personal Activity Preference** plan. Both, the group, and the 1-1, activity schedules that you create from now on will centre around those preferences, i.e. the residents will tell you what activities they want for the year – and what could be more person-centred than that?

Most of the ideas won't require you to have a large budget either.

The **Resident Personal Activity Preference** plan is an essential tool that will:

a) Ensure that the home offers activities that the residents actually *want*.

b) Protect the staff from any claims that the home is not providing meaningful, person-centred activities.

On the next page you will find a full-sized **Resident Personal Activity Preference** form for you to photocopy. You will need to print a form for each resident.

 But <u>BEFORE</u> you get going on the forms, it's important that you take some time to read the accompanying notes.

RESIDENT PERSONAL ACTIVITY PREFERENCE RECORD

RESIDENT'S NAME

DATE THAT THIS FORM WAS COMPLETED (Update form annually)

WHAT ACTIVITIES WOULD YOU LIKE TO DO IF A MEMBER OF STAFF WAS MADE AVAILABLE TO YOU PERSONALLY? (APPROX 30 MINS)

WHAT GROUP ACTIVITIES AND EVENTS WOULD YOU DEFINITELY ATTEND IF THEY WERE MADE AVAILABLE?

SIGNATURE OF RESIDENT: SIGNED ON THE RESIDENT'S BEHALF WITH THEIR PERMISSION, BY:

....   SIGNED BY.........................SIGNATURE.....................................

DATE ABOVE ACTIVITY WAS OFFERED TO THIS RESIDENT + NAME OF STAFF MEMBER WHO ASKED THEM TO ATTEND ON THE DAY	WHICH OF THE ABOVE ACTIVITIES WAS OFFERED?	TIME OF DAY THE ACTIVITY WAS OFFERED	RESIDENT'S RESPONSE: PARTICIPATED (P) DECLINED (D) WAS ILL (S)
1.			
2.			
3.			
4.			
5.			

Important notes for the RESIDENT PERSONAL ACTIVITY RECORD

You will see that the FIRST SECTION on the form asks the resident how they would like to spend a personal 30-minute activity session with a member of the team.

The SECOND SECTION asks what group activities and events they would definitely attend if they were made available. This seems like a pretty straight forward set of questions, right? With straight forward answers? If only it were that simple!
In fact, this is the part of the process where many activity schedules fail.

To explain further, consider this:

Have you ever asked the residents what activities they would like to see on the activity schedule, and then painstakingly arranged them, only to find that nobody wants to attend on the day?

Every... Single... Day!

Soul destroying isn't it! But you're not alone!

There is a simple reason this happens!

The residents are most likely giving you a list of things they *like* doing, but what they might not have considered is:

Whether they are still _able_ or even _willing_ to participate in that particular activity!

In many cases, the residents might simply be sharing with you, happy memories of activities they used to enjoy doing with friends and family. They probably haven't thought about how they feel about doing the same activity under their *current* circumstances.
After careful consideration, they may discover many reasons for not wanting to participate in an activity that they once enjoyed, e.g.

  I.   They might be happy just relaxing and doing simpler, more reflective things with their time these days.

  II.   The activity might make them feel upset and frustrated that they cannot physically do it anymore.

  III. It might remind them of the family members, friends, and happy times that they miss.

  IV.   They may feel embarrassed about incontinence and other health issues that they don't want others to know about.

        There are countless other reasons that they might not wish to share with you.

Below, are two real-life case studies, experienced by an activity coordinator when filling out a resident's Personal Activity Preference record:

 1.   Resident, Mary told the activity coordinator that she has always loved gardening and flower arranging, and said that she'd love to do them again. However, when a flower arranging session was organised for the residents, Mary refused to attend, leaving the activity coordinator feeling frustrated. A few days later, while sitting talking with Mary, the activity coordinator casually brought the conversation round to why Mary had declined to attend the flower arranging session. Mary disclosed that she didn't enjoy doing it anymore as she lacks the dexterity to hold the flowers, so it makes her feel angry and 'old.' The reality of Mary's physical disability only hit her on the morning of the session, and she didn't want to say anything as she felt too upset.

 2.   Resident, Tom often sat in his room feeling sad. He told the activity coordinator that he desperately missed his friends and going to his local club. He said that he wishes that he could still go every week. When the activity coordinator asked Tom whether he would like to be taken there by the activity staff every week, he declined. When the activity coordinator dug a little deeper, Tom revealed that he didn't want his friends at the club to know that he was living in a residential home now, and that he needed to be pushed in a wheelchair. He was also really embarrassed about his incontinence issues.

Often the resident will not disclose these deeply personal feelings, and instead decide that it is easier to just not turn up to the activity.

For this reason, the SECOND SECTION of the Resident Personal Activity Preference form, underlines the point - 'group activities and events you would _definitely_ attend.'

This is to prompt the staff to have a deeper discussion with each resident about whether the activities they mention would *still* make them happy under their *current* circumstances. It is important to have an open and supportive conversation with that person to understand their needs and preferences.

If capacity or physical health leads to a resident rejecting activities that they previously loved, then suggest similar alternatives so that they can be involved in the activity on a slightly different, but less upsetting level.

The below table shows a list of possible alternatives to popular physical activities that the residents might enjoy:

ACTIVITY	MEANINGFUL ALTERNATIVES
Theatre trips	<ul><li>Invite local amateur dramatics groups to come in and do a few scenes/ songs from their shows.</li><li>Play a DVD, or download, of a theatre production of the resident's choice.</li></ul>
Reading stories/poetry/ magazines/ newspapers	<ul><li>Identify the books that a resident with poor vision once enjoyed reading, and find a copy to read to them.</li><li>Read short stories / newspaper headlines to a larger group of residents each Friday.</li></ul>
Sewing/Crafts	<ul><li>The knowledgeable resident who can no longer take part, could instruct an activity staff member in a craft/sewing project. Tap into their knowledge and expertise, and collaborate to complete the item.</li></ul>
The resident used to fly planes in the RAF during the war	<ul><li>Get them to tell you stories about their time in the RAF and ask them lots of questions.</li><li>Borrow a book about the wartime RAF from your local library, read part of it, and ask the resident to share their knowledge of the content.</li><li>Borrow a DVD from the library, or find some archive films of 40s/50s forces aircraft online to watch.</li></ul>
The resident had a mechanical engineering job/or hobby	<ul><li>Bring in a simple broken mechanical item that the resident can help you to repair (Or they can supervise you)</li><li>Obtain/buy a 3D block puzzle where you can slot the pieces together to build a car etc. (good for those with poor eyesight)</li></ul>
Flower arranging and gardening activities	<ul><li>Ask a local horticulturalist to come in and do a seasonal talk on plants and flowers each quarter. They could bring in some examples for the residents to hold.</li><li>Create a small trough of soil and get the interested resident to plant the seeds. They can keep it in their room if they wish and watch them grow. The staff can help them water it regularly.</li></ul>

What other kinds of activities might your residents be interested in? Have a look on their Me and My Life forms for some ideas of what they might ask to do. What meaningful alternatives could you suggest to them if needed?

	ACTIVITY ENJOYED	MEANINGFUL ALTERNATIVES
1		
2		
3		
4		
5		

NOW, WITH THIS IN MIND, IT'S TIME TO GO AND VISIT THE RESIDENTS AND COMPLETE TASK 5!

 TASK 5: Fill out a Resident Personal Activity Preference Record with each resident - considering whether they are still able and willing to attend the activities they suggest. Have a few ideas of your own to suggest to them too - based on what you know about them from their Me and My Life form. Once complete, ask the resident to sign it, or sign it on their behalf if necessary (and with their permission).

The requests on these forms will enable you to create your weekly activity timetables.

PLEASE DON'T FORGET! At the bottom of the form, you should write down the date you offered the requested activity to that particular resident and note whether they attended or not. It is important to keep these records up to date as it evidences your person-centred approach to activities and will also protect you from any unfair external criticisms of your department's activity provision.

Once you have a completed Resident Personal Activity Preference Record for each resident, you can move onto **SECTION 2 – Creating strong activity schedules.**

SECTION 2

Creating strong activity schedules

Firstly, take all of the **group** activities suggested on the Resident Personal Activity Preference Records and create a 4-week, person-centred activities schedule.

But first, let's take a deeper look at how to schedule these ideas across the week.

Start by categorising each of the suggested activities under a specific heading - highlighting its main physical and mental health benefit for the residents.

The following column headings would be a useful place to start:

1. MOBILITY
   e.g. Increases mobility | lessens risk of falling | Promotes overall wellbeing.

2. MENTAL STIMULATION
   e.g. Helps memory and recall | Self-empowerment | Promotes happiness.

3. EMOTIONAL WELLBEING
   e.g. Boosts self-worth | Aids relaxation | Gives physical human connection.

4. HOBBIES AND RECREATION
   e.g. Connects resident to self-identity | Promotes happiness | Increases dexterity.

5. EMPOWERMENT AND SELF-PRIDE
   e.g. Promotes happiness | Stimulates brain activity | Increases motivation

6. FRESH AIR AND OUTDOORS
   e.g. Physical health | Mental stimulation | Increases recall and wellbeing

7. FAMILY VALUES
   e.g. Connection with self-identity | Increases recall | Family interactions.

Use the table on the next page to categorise your list of activities. (You might want to photocopy the table first) Some activities will fall under more than one category.

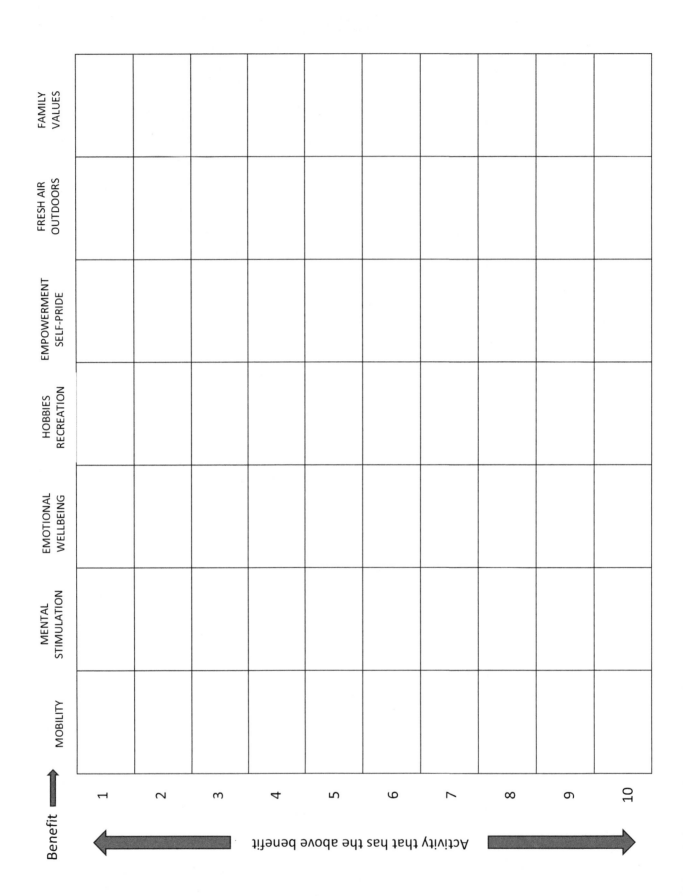

	MOBILITY	MENTAL STIMULATION	EMOTIONAL WELLBEING	HOBBIES RECREATION	EMPOWERMENT SELF-PRIDE	FRESH AIR OUTDOORS	FAMILY VALUES
1							
2							
3							
4							
5							
6							
7							
8							
9							
10							

Benefit →

← Activity that has the above benefit →

ACTIVITY SCHEDULE: FOR THE ACTIVITY TEAM'S REFERENCE
(The residents will receive an edited version)

 Now, it is time to plan your weekly timetable by taking a selection of activities from each category and scheduling them across the week. To begin with, you might want to focus on one particular benefit each day, as shown in the example below. This will help you to keep it balanced.

You can also schedule in your 1-1 sessions with the residents, your paperwork time, and extra beneficial activities such as exercises, mobile shop, hairdresser etc, to plan your team's work week.

Here is an example of a well-balanced, person-centred weekly activity schedule:

	MONDAY	TUESDAY	WEDNESDAY	THURSDAY	FRIDAY	SATURDAY	SUNDAY
BENEFIT ->	MOBILITY	MENTAL STIMULATION	EMOTIONAL WELLBEING	HOBBIES RECREATION	EMPOWERMENT SELF-PRIDE	FRESH AIR OUTDOORS	FAMILY VALUES
WEEK 1	(DELIVER 'PAST TIMES' NEWSPAPER to each resident - 1st of each Month)		(HAND OUT NEW QUIZ SHEET - EVERY WED TO EACH RESIDENT)		(HAND OUT PUZZLE SHEET EVERY FRI TO EVERY RESIDENT) * HAIRDRESSER 8.30am -1pm		
9.45 - 11.30am	MOBILE SHOP (Every Monday) visit every resident	1-1 QUIZ with Cliff in his room.	ALL DAY 1-1 PAMPERING (15-20 mins per resident) Choose from: Hand or foot massage	GROUP GARDENING CLUB potting geraniums	PHOTO ALBUM reminiscing with Joan in the small lounge	1-1 WALK to the shops with Roger to buy magazines/ books	GROUP SING ALONG in main lounge
11.45 - 12.15	GROUP EXERCISES in small lounge	GROUP QUIZ + reminiscing. In TV room.	Hair brushed and styled Shoulder or head massage	GROUP HOBBY CLUB (low capacity) Painting in dining room	GROUP REMINISCING Jobs the residents had. in main lounge.	GROUP WALK around the garden	GROUP QUIZ - invite any visitors to take part. in main lounge
2.30 - 4PM	1-1 EXERCISES with Beryl in her room	GROUP TALK: The social history of nursery rhymes. in main lounge.	Pedicures Manicures Meditation Make-up In lounge or resident's preferred space.	GROUP AFTERNOON FILM with cake and tea In TV lounge. *Activity staff to use this time to plan following week/month activities/ book entertainers etc.	1-1 MODEL MAKING with Tom in the small lounge. 1-1 CLEARING OUT old clothes with Joyce in her room	GROUP SHORT STORY in the garden + and summary of the week's newspaper headlines.	GROUP SUNDAY AFTERNOON TEA with scones/ sandwiches made by kitchen + 1940s music and dancing. in family lounge.

On the next page you will find a blank copy of this activity schedule to photocopy. Create your own weekly activities timetable under the seven headings, or mix them up.

DAY - - - -> DATE - - - ->	MONDAY	TUESDAY	WEDNESDAY	THURSDAY	FRIDAY	SATURDAY	SUNDAY
BENEFIT - -> TIME ↓	MOBILITY AND INTERACTION	MENTAL STIMULATION AND INTERACTION	PAMPERING / WELLBEING DAY	HOBBIES AND RECREATION DAY	LIFE STORIES DAY	FRESH AIR AND OUTDOORS DAY	FAMILY AND TRADITIONAL SUNDAY
Morning							
Afternoon							
Evening							

> **TOP TIP:** Schedule the regular weekly activities on the **same day and time each week** e.g. exercises, the mobile shop, film afternoon, games afternoon etc. It will give the residents a welcome routine to plan their week around. It will also allow family members to schedule visits during the fun activities like the weekly quiz or sing-alongs.

Next, draw up a simple version of the activity schedule for the residents.

Please don't put planned resident 1-1s on the resident's copy of the activity schedule as it confuses them. (There is a separate 1-1 activity schedule for you to photocopy on the following pages) Hand out an activity schedule to each resident on a Friday afternoon so that they can plan their week ahead. It is also useful to put additional copies on the public noticeboards for the care staff and families to view. The kitchen staff would find a weekly copy useful too, so that they can plan meals around special events/ daytrips out etc.

THE RESIDENT'S COPY OF THE WEEKLY ACTIVITY SCHEDULE

The copy of the weekly activity schedule given to residents should be simple, and show similar detail to the example below, but we encourage you to design your own template that is appropriate to your particular care setting.

[Insert house name] ACTIVITY SCHEDULE **W/C 12th June 2023**

Activities Team this week: Vicky and Nigel

Monday 12th June

9am	**PAST TIMES Newspapers delivered**
9.45am – 11.30am	**MOBILE SHOP** coming round. With Vicky
11.45am – 12.15pm	**SEATED EXERCISES** with **Frank Sinatra** music. In small lounge. With Vicky

Tuesday 13th June

11.45am – 12.15pm	**QUIZ + REMINISCING** in TV lounge. With Nigel
3pm – 4pm	**HISTORY TALK: The Social History of Nursery Rhymes** in main lounge. With Nigel

Wednesday 14th June

9am	**New Quiz Sheet being delivered to rooms**

	PAMPERING SESSIONS all day. With Vicky and Nigel
9.45- 4pm	Choose your 1 x 20 min session from: Hand Massage | Foot Massage | Head Massage | Shoulder Massage |Hair Brushed | Make-Up done | Guided Meditation | Manicure | Pedicure In small lounge or rooms. Bookings taken by activities staff in the AM

Thursday 15th June

10.30am – 11.30am	**GARDENING CLUB –** Potting geraniums in small garden | Small lounge. With Nigel
11.45am – 12.15	**HOBBY CLUB – Extra Support - Painting** in dining room. With Nigel
2.30pm – 4.30pm	**AFTERNOON FILM with tea and cake** 'CALAMITY JANE' starring Doris Day in TV lounge

Friday 16th June

9am	**New puzzle sheet being delivered to rooms**
9am – 12pm	**HAIRDRESSER** in all morning In the salon – With Maureen
11am – 12.15pm	**REMINISCING** – Sharing memories of the jobs we used to have. In main lounge. With Vicky

Saturday 17th June

11am – 12.15pm	**GROUP WALK AROUND THE GARDENS.** With Vicky
2.30pm - 3.30pm	**SHORT STORY AND NEWSPAPER HEADLINES** In garden. With Nigel

Sunday 19th June

10.30am – 11.15am	**SING-ALONG** In main lounge. With Vicky
11.45am – 12.15pm	**QUIZ** – For residents and visiting families. In main lounge. With Vicky
3pm-4.30pm	**AFTERNOON TEA** with 1940s music and optional dancing. In family lounge. With Vicky

RESIDENT 1-1 ACTIVITY SCHEDULE
& DAILY RECORD OF ACTIVITIES

On the following two pages you will find two extra documents to photocopy and keep in files:

a) A **Resident Activity 30 min 1-1 timetable.** To schedule the resident's 1-1 time with the activity staff. (Try and book each resident in for a 1-1 at least once a month if possible)

b) **A Daily Record of Activities.** To be filled in daily. Documenting the activities that each resident has participated in that day. (It is important that you note on the form if a resident has been alone in their room all day, or hasn't been visited by the activity team, so that this can be addressed on the next shift)

RESIDENT 30 min 1-1 activity schedule – Schedule time with each resident, and sign once you have completed the 30 min activity.

Month: **Year:**

1st	2nd	3rd	4th	5th	6th	7th
Resident: Activity: Staff member:	Resident: Activity: Staff member:	Resident: Activity: Staff member:	Resident: Activity: Staff member:	Resident: Activity: Staff member:	Resident: Activity: Staff member:	Resident: Activity: Staff member:
8th	**9th**	**10th**	**11th**	**12th**	**13th**	**14th**
Resident: Activity: Staff member:	Resident: Activity: Staff member:	Resident: Activity: Staff member:	Resident: Activity: Staff member:	Resident: Activity: Staff member:	Resident: Activity: Staff member:	Resident: Activity: Staff member:
15th	**16th**	**17th**	**18th**	**19th**	**20th**	**21st**
Resident: Activity: Staff member:	Resident: Activity: Staff member:	Resident: Activity: Staff member:	Resident: Activity: Staff member:	Resident: Activity: Staff member:	Resident: Activity: Staff member:	Resident: Activity: Staff member:
22nd	**23rd**	**24th**	**25th**	**26th**	**27th**	**28th**
Resident: Activity: Staff member:	Resident: Activity: Staff member:	Resident: Activity: Staff member:	Resident: Activity: Staff member:	Resident: Activity: Staff member:	Resident: Activity: Staff member:	Resident: Activity: Staff member:
29th	**30th**	**31st**				
Resident: Activity: Staff member:	Resident: Activity: Staff member:	Resident: Activity: Staff member:				

Printable Resource from The Ultimate Handbook for Activity Coordinators

DAILY RECORD OF ACTIVITIES FOR ALL RESIDENTS

Date	Resident	Activity Y or N + details	General mood today

Cont'd over

PAPERWORK AND FILES THAT YOU SHOULD NOW HAVE

So, hopefully you now feel confident, and well equipped to deliver meaningful, person-centred activities that the residents have asked for. If not, have a look over the tasks once more.

NOTE: Your activity paperwork does not need to be any more complex or time-consuming than the documents provided in this handbook. These documents have been well received by elderly care home managers over the UK, and by governing bodies during inspections. If you keep on top of it, your life will be made much easier!

To double check you have what you need, below is a recap of the paperwork files you should now have in your office.

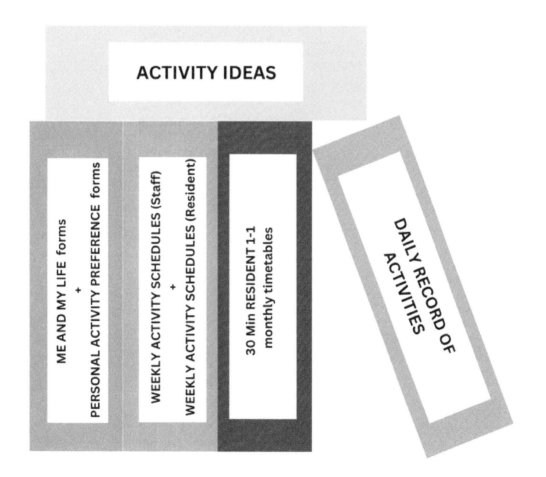

THE CONTENTS OF EACH FILE IN DETAIL:

FILE 1:
a) Completed **Me and My Life** forms for <u>every</u> resident.

Complete forms a & b within <u>one week</u> of a resident moving into the care home, and refer to them **weekly** when planning your activities.

b) Completed and signed **Personal Activity Preference Records** for <u>every</u> resident.

Signed at the bottom whenever a resident has been offered an activity they requested.

FILE 2:
a) **Weekly Activity Schedules** for the activity staff.

Forms a & b to be completed whenever planning and scheduling activities.

b) **Weekly Activity Schedules** for the residents.

*Keep completed copies of each form for 5 years – or whatever your care home's policy is on this (Check directly with the home's manager)

FILE 3: **Resident 30 min 1-1 monthly schedules.**

To be **signed** daily whenever a 1-1 has been completed.

*Keep completed copies for 5 years – or follow your care home's policy on this.

FILE 4: **Daily Activity Record forms**

To be filled out **daily** at the end of every shift.

FILE 5: **A collection of activity ideas**

Create a file of activity ideas and keep any relevant resources with them. This will help you to fill any gaps in the activity schedules.
To start you off, on page 53 you will find a list of what we consider to be the **Top 10 Most Successful Activities** and resources in elderly care homes.

WALL PLANNER: It is also useful to keep an easily viewable year planner on your workspace wall so that the activities team can see at a glance, any upcoming special events you need to plan for, including:

- National holidays
- Anniversaries
- Birthdays
- Religious festivals
- Jubilees
- VE Day
- Easter holidays
- Annual fairs and local celebrations
- Visits from entertainers
- Day Trips
- Royal celebrations
- And other important dates that the residents asked you to remember on their Me and My Life forms.

An activity / events wall planner is also a useful tool for the care staff, as it allows them to see any special events coming up, and plan routine appointments and staff availability around them.

Still struggling to get your residents motivated?

THE ENTHUSIASM STRUGGLE IS REAL!

We hear you! You've followed every process in this training handbook and done everything you can to get to know your residents, and then spent hours planning the activities that they have asked for, but you still end up spending the activity hour alone, kicking dusty tumbleweed across the floor, while Mavis snores away in the corner! So, what do you do? You've got your manager insisting that the residents need to be engaged in fantastic activities, but all you're getting from the residents are those four little words that make an activity coordinator's heart sink, 'I can't be bothered!' These are the times when our morale generally sinks to rock bottom!

It can be a daunting and frustrating feeling, can't it? Most of us came into this job wanting to make people's lives better, but we often feel like giving up because no one is interested in our efforts, and then we get worried that we'll lose our jobs! Well, we have written this section just for you, to let you know that you're not alone. We see you! If you are feeling unappreciated right now, let us tell you that activity coordinators across the world are feeling just the same as you. We're in this together! Don't give up!

We have a plan to help you!

How you can turn this situation around!

 First go back to the checklist: ☑

1. Are the activities what the residents have asked for? ☐

2. Are the activities empowering for your residents? Do they make them feel positive? ☐

3. Are the activities stimulating enough to engage the most outgoing residents? ☐

4. Are the activities well balanced and interesting to all the residents? (i.e. not just to the same few, easy to please residents) ☐

5. Have all residents been given their own personal activity timetable to refer to? ☐

6. Do you remind each resident in good time that the activity is about to start? ☐

If you have ticked all of the above boxes, and the residents still say that they don't want to take part, then make sure that you have recorded their response on their personal preference form, and on the daily activities record.

The home will naturally go through stages of quietness and apathy, depending on the personalities of the residents you have at any given time. You sometimes just have to ride this out until an outgoing resident moves in and shifts the energy in a positive direction.

❗   Important note: Please Read! ...Then Read Again!

When residents are asked by their family, or the management, or by CQC inspectors, about the activities that are provided at the residential home, it is standard that some will complain that there is nothing to interest them, or that they never see the activities team. However unfair this seems, you as the activity coordinator will be held accountable. That's why it is <u>essential</u> that you complete the **Daily Record of Activities**, and the **Resident Personal Activity Preference Records** every day to evidence the dates you put on the activities they personally asked for, and what their response was to the invite. <u>Those forms will protect you</u> against unfair accusations and will massively reduce your personal stress levels.

Aside from the normal personality dynamics affecting the overall mood swings in the home, there may be other reasons why the residents won't attend activities. These reasons are not always obvious.

- Morning activities are generally less attended as many residents have a slow start. There is sometimes a carer shortage, resulting in it taking longer to get the residents up, washed and ready. For this reason, it is usually better to plan popular activities, entertainer visits, and trips out, in the afternoons when all the residents are about.

- The less mobile residents may have to rely on a member of staff to assist them to the activity room. The carers are often overstretched and unavailable, so if possible, visit each resident 20 mins before the activities start to see if they need assistance.

- The residents are mostly elderly, and their energy levels are naturally lower than yours, so it might be useful to move the activity to the room where most of them are already sitting. Then they don't have to move from their comfy chair, and you will have a captive audience that will begin to engage in the activity.

- It may be that a resident is genuinely happy in their own company, thinking their own thoughts, listening to a radio programme, or reading a book etc. They might not need any other mental stimulus. As long as you pop in for regular visits and check on them, then it's fine. You can log on their daily activity sheet that you went to see them and that they were happy reading etc. No one will criticise you for that.

- In general, our motivation to take part in activities usually comes from our being in a cheerful mood. You can help to keep the resident's mood up by making them laugh whenever you see them, or by saying something that makes them feel good about themselves. Impromptu sing-alongs also keep the morale of residents and staff up. If you are jolly, the residents will enjoy spending time with you, and be more likely to come to the activities you provide.

  Note: It might sound harsh but it is vital that you don't bring your own personal problems into the home. The residents will sense your low morale and it will affect any motivation or enthusiasm they have for joining in activities. However, it's not always that easy is it? A care home setting can sometimes feel like a pressure cooker about to explode. So, the next few pages will offer you some coping mechanisms to help reduce your stress levels at work.

KEEPING YOURSELF MOTIVATED

We've all had one of those days! When we walk into work to discover that the staff are all stressed out, the boss is in a bad mood, and the residents are bombarding us with a list of complaints - before we've even taken our coat off.

For some of us, *'one of those days'* turns into *'one of those weeks,'* and sometimes even *'one of those years.'* - where being in the firing line of everyone's emotions has sapped our energy and left us feeling completely demotivated and run down. That can often be the sad reality of working in a care environment, and we all go through it. We feel the impact that bad energy has on us, and how it can crush our morale very quickly, but we don't always stop to think about how *our* low mood might affect others. Especially the residents, whose lives now mostly revolve around the residential home. It only takes one stressed out member of staff to send their whole world spiralling down to a place of upset.

So, how do you prevent your annoyance with someone (Either inside or outside work) impacting on your work environment?

A useful tool is to reframe how you feel about stressful situations. The reality is that:

You cannot control other people's behaviour.
You can only control how you deal with the blows.

And it is 100% true! Trying to stop a person behaving in a certain way is generally a pointless exercise and will only lead to further arguments. But by making the decision – *and it is only a matter of deciding* - that you will not let their unreasonable, emotional behaviour impact on you, you can become skilled at letting it bounce off you. Of course, it takes a little practice!

Try saying this mantra to yourself, next time someone is giving you a hard time.

"Your bad mood is not mine to own!"

… and refuse to let it in.

Then quickly make the decision:

1. Is what is upsetting them <u>anything to do with you</u>? i.e. is it something that you can easily fix?

2. Or, is what is upsetting them <u>nothing to do with you</u>? i.e. Are you just the poor soul who happened to wander into their eyeline at the wrong moment?

Stress busting strategy 1: If their low mood is something you can fix, then go ahead and do so. Swallow your pride if you need to. It will allow everyone to move on quickly, and with limited upset.

Stress busting strategy 2: If their low mood is nothing to do with you, then there is zero point in letting it impact on you. Instead, imagine a protective bubble surrounding you. Shut the bubble door and let their words and bad energy bounce away from its surface. Because 'Their bad mood is not yours to own.' Their bad mood is a result of what is going on in their own lives, and <u>not yours</u>! Remember that. They can only get to you if you open the door of your bubble and let them in.

The 'protective bubble' method is great at lowering stress and keeping motivation high because it gives us a sense of perspective - a moment to assess the situation before we get pulled into our reactive, and often destructive, *fight or flight* mode.

Negative emotions in others are usually a result of the decisions they have made, not *yours*, so it's your choice whether you allow them into your sacred quiet space or not. Actively blocking them is a very powerful way of taking back control of the situation.

WHY IS IT IMPORTANT TO REDUCE OUR PERSONAL STRESS LEVELS?

Because it destroys our physical and mental health

Stress has been medically proved to make our bodies sick, so it's important that we avoid letting it in.

The science: When we feel attacked in some way, our body releases a chemical called cortisol – also known as the 'stress hormone.'

Cortisol is what makes us feel agitated, giving us that fight or flight energy boost that allows us to flee a threatening situation. Historically, our ancestors would have used that burst of cortisol to outrun predators, and then taken time to recover, as too much cortisol causes our cells to become sick. We're not designed to cope with stress very often.

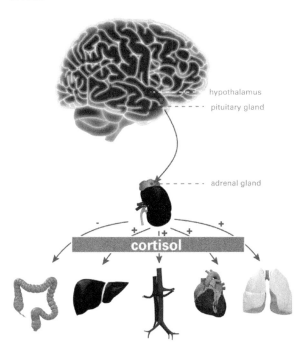

Yet, the demands of the modern world mean that we now release cortisol into our cells most days. We are no longer chased by predators but we do feel 'attacked' continually by work deadlines, money worries, inconsiderate drivers, family worries, social pressures etc, keeping our bodies in a constant fight or flight (cortisol-releasing) mode.

Even excessive gaming releases cortisol due to the challenges built into them.

Cortisol directly affects our organs and has been linked to many of the illnesses we suffer today, including high blood pressure, depression, and cancer.

So, it's important that we give consideration as to what / and whose stress we allow into our bodies. Are you currently allowing other people's bad behaviour to make *your* body sick? As a counter thought, could your anxiety be raising other people's stress levels?

LET GO OF OTHER PEOPLE'S PROBLEMS

Another tool that helps reduce stress, involves harnessing the power of empathy. How it works: Create a story around what the offending person might be experiencing in their lives, which is making them behave like this. It might even turn out to be true! By forcing yourself to 'feel sorry' for the person, your own stress levels will lower.

Here are three stages of thinking about a problem. Stages 1, 2 and 3 will help you to step out of a conflict quickly:

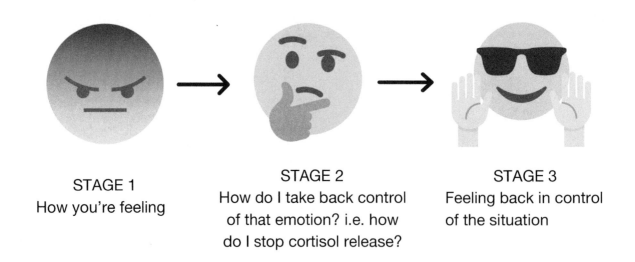

STAGE 1
How you're feeling

STAGE 2
How do I take back control of that emotion? i.e. how do I stop cortisol release?

STAGE 3
Feeling back in control of the situation

Take a look at the table on the next page.

A. The left-hand column (Stage 1) lists the things that might stress you out.

B. The middle column (Stage 2) gives you an example of a thought process to protect you from their negative behaviour/emotion i.e. take back control.

C. The right-hand column (Stage 3) offers ways of diffusing the stressful situation.

	Stressful encounter you might have	What I can tell myself so that I don't 'own' their stress and release cortisol into my body	Ways to take back control
1.	A resident continually complains that I never do anything for them.	The resident may be feeling very low about all that they have lost. They might be desperate for love, and to have control over something.	Sit with them for a few minutes and hold their hand.
2.	My manager complains that I'm not providing enough activities.	They are getting pressure from their bosses /board members to get a good CQC report.	Show the manager all the paperwork you have in place e.g. The Resident Activity Preference forms and person-centred activity timetable.
3.	My manager says that not enough residents are attending activities.	They are stressed out because one of the resident's family members have complained that their parent is not being mentally stimulated. They are also getting bombarded with other email complaints about a hundred different things that are nothing to do with you.	As above, show the manager all the documentary evidence, showing that you are providing activities that they have asked for. This will reassure them.
4.	A particular member of staff is always talking about me behind my back.	They are probably feeling bored, unfulfilled, or threatened in some way. They might have problems at home.	Next time you see them, stop and ask them how they are, and be really friendly. Empathise with the fact that they have got a lot of work to do. You'll be surprised how quickly you can get this person onside.
5.	The driver of another car cut me up on the way to work.	They probably didn't even see you. They may have been worried about a sick child or relative. They might have just been made redundant.	Most people are actually nice, so give them the benefit of the doubt and you'll be able to let it go.

Now have a think about the things that might stress you out at work – especially the things that have impacted on your morale, and come up with some thought processes to help you take back control.

	Stressful encounter	What I can tell myself so that I don't 'own' their stress and release cortisol into my body	Ways to take back control
1.			
2.			
3.			
4.			
5.			

This exercise is a useful life tool to alleviate stress that is not yours to own. It is useful inside and outside of work - especially when you can't control the situation.

SECTION 4

In this section you will find lots of extra activity ideas to meet the physical and emotional needs of your residents. As many of you work alone, and with zero budget, you will be relieved to hear that most of these ideas need limited staff and money. Note: Think about how you could also design an activity around your own hobbies e.g. Do you play an instrument? Could you give the residents a mini concert? Are you a wildlife photographer? Could you do a short talk with some photos you have taken? Have a think and maybe add your own ideas to the following lists.

 # Activities that Increase Mobility

1. Seated exercises

2. Walking around the home / garden / outdoors

3. Assisted exercises

4. Shoulder / hand / foot massages

5. Dancing

6. Going out shopping

7. Ball throwing and catching

8. Encouraging residents to leave their room for meals

9. Gardening – or create a small allotment using crates and compost

10. Lawn or carpet bowls

11. Seated balloon tennis

12. Adding arm actions to a sing-along

13. Pulse-squeeze the arm of a chair or beanbag for finger dexterity

14. Finger-moving exercises such as knitting, or doing jigsaw puzzles

15. Encouraging residents to dress themselves wherever possible

16. Mini carpet golf

17. Playing musical instruments

18. Kneading dough or mixing cake batter

19. Clay model making

20. Days out to tourist attractions

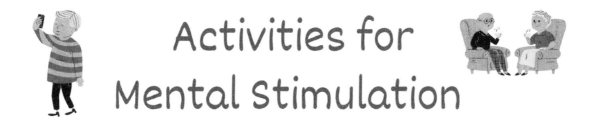

Activities for Mental Stimulation

1. Quizzes and memory games

2. Group guessing games e.g. giant hangman or Play Your Cards Right

3. Sing-alongs

4. Conversations, sharing memories of work, hobbies, family etc

5. Board games and table puzzles

6. Going out into the community

7. Home visits by entertainers, schools, local historians etc

8. Encouraging a monthly day out with their family

9. Pub meals

10. Boat trips

11. Using Google Maps to see the streets where they lived/ grew up

12. Ball games

13. Recording a resident's life story (Find resources on page 71)

14. Making up stories as a group (Find resources on page 54)

15. Reading newspapers, books and magazines

16. Arts, crafts, painting sessions

17. Gardening activities

18. Enjoying history documentaries and books from the resident's era

19. Looking at old photographs and discussing memories

20. Group discussions on specific topics of interest

Activities for Pampering and Emotional Well-being

1. Manicure or pedicure sessions

2. Hair brushing and styling

3. Light shoulder and head massages

4. Hand massages

5. Make-up application

6. Sampling interesting food and drink

7. Afternoon tea

8. Arrange family sports day/ garden parties in the summer

9. Film afternoon with individual bags/bowls of sweets

10. Soft music with drinks, nibbles, and conversation

11. Pampering hand and face masks

12. Soap making session

13. Chocolate making

14. Light facials

15. Friday evening take-away meal club

16. Cream cake afternoon

17. Birthday party for each resident

18. Walking around a local green space

19. Reading out a short story or poem to the group, with a cup of tea

20. Afternoon tea, with cakes on a stand

Activities around Hobbies and Recreation

1. Tapping a golf ball into a circle of string on the floor

2. Knit and natter group, or a still life drawing/painting session

3. Fairground games e.g. hoopla or hook a duck for prizes + candyfloss

4. Group sing along with printed song sheets

5. Group discussion on hobbies and pastimes that your residents liked

6. Flipchart hangman – use song titles/proverbs/countries etc

7. Ball and beanbag throwing games

8. Racing bets – get old race videos from the internet to bet on

9. Chair football using a light football. Give commentary for fun

10. Flower arranging session – with a local enthusiast giving a talk

11. Afternoon beer/wine sampling club

12. Vintage clothes exhibition + discussion around favourite fashions

13. Gardening. Vegetable and flower seed planting, and harvesting

14. History session with local enthusiast giving a talk

15. Ask the local Scout / Brownies etc. group to visit

16. Invite a primary school to visit the home and give a concert

17. Invite local amateur dramatic groups to perform a short show.

18. Visit a free local museum or attraction

19. Boardgames and puzzles

20. Create themed afternoons with relevant food and activities

Activities for Empowerment and Self-Pride

1.   Begin writing life story – Instructions on page 71

2.   Group quiz – shout out the answers. Free quiz sheet on page 58

3.   Make up a group story – Instructions on page 54

4.   Group conversation about jobs they had, or school memories etc.

5.   An activity where a resident shares their expertise on a subject

6.   Group sing-along

7.   Organise a 1-1 activity that a resident has chosen for themselves

8.   Ask a resident for advice on something, and make them feel needed

9.   Organise a group music or dancing session

10. Ask a quieter resident to teach you their favourite poem or story

11. Use Google Maps to show a resident the streets they grew up on

12. Look through photo albums and share memories

13. Look at picture books of their town / school during a specific era

14. Find old photos online of the jobs or hobbies etc. that a resident had

15. Organise a lively game that everyone can take part in

16. Attend a local history talk to allow the residents to share memories

17. Visit a stately home or museum with familiar household objects

18. Encourage family members to visit and take part in the weekly quiz

19. Assist a resident in doing chores in their room. Let them lead.

20. Offer the resident's problem-solving puzzles to do on their own

Activities in the Outdoors and Fresh Air

1.   Chair exercises (with the window open on warm days)

2.   A walk around the garden

3.   A walk to the local shops

4.   Get the bus into town or the next village

5.   Stroll around the local park or green space

6.   Hold an outdoor quiz

7.   Grow flowers and veg in a raised bed/planter

8.   Enjoy coffee and cake at a local café

9.   Take a trip out to a garden centre

10.   Visit a museum, zoo, or stately home

11.   Take afternoon tea in the garden

12.   Encourage group conversation outside

13.   Play outdoor games such as skittles/ beanbag hoop target

14.   Golf – create a simple golf putting green in the grounds

15.   Organise a vintage car enthusiast to visit the home

16.   Attend the local annual celebrations and fetes etc.

17.   Hold a royal celebration street party

18.   Walk by a lake or river

19.   Paint still life pictures outside

20.   Get some seed and feed the local birds / ducks etc.

Activities around Family Values

1. Sunday afternoon tea with scones and nostalgic music

2. Family quizzes – promotes family bonding

3. Attend a local church service (or other appropriate religious services)

4. Group board games

5. Afternoon film with bags/bowls of sweets (Close curtains for atmosphere)

6. Group sing-along with traditional songs

7. Reminiscing about childhood e.g. favourite toys/ visiting grandparents

8. Reminiscing about family e.g. holidays / weekend pastimes

9. Crafts such as knitting and card making

10. Reading a short story or familiar poem aloud for the residents

11. Looking at the resident's photo albums with them

12. Flower arranging / gardening club

13. Discussing the headlines and articles in the Sunday newspapers

14. Placing memorabilia on the dinner tables to promote memory sharing

15. Having a Sunday afternoon mobile pub trolley (Where appropriate)

16. Organise a visit from an entertainer

17. Encourage room visits between residents who are friends

18. Discuss old photos of the local area and what it looked like

19. An afternoon walk somewhere local and nice

20. Encouraging family / friends and the resident's pets to visit

SECTION 5: Activities for residents with dementia

You've so far been doing a lot of groundwork, getting to know your residents which, of course, underpins absolutely every activity that you do - from motivating them to attend activities, through to creating easily managed records that CQC and your manager will approve of.

But if you're working with people with dementia, you might feel that connecting with a resident's emotional needs is harder. In cases of advanced dementia, an individual might not be able to articulate what they enjoy. Their verbal responses might be limited, or their mood may vary throughout the day with no indication as to why. As a result, the needs of these residents might be side-lined in favour of the needs of the more vocal residents. It is important that we don't let this happen.

What can you do to ensure that residents living with dementia receive daily person-centred activities too?

1. Refer to their 'me and my life' form and find out what their hobbies were, what they did for a living, or where they used to live. Ask a family member or friend to help you fill in the gaps if there isn't one in their file.

2. Then use that information to create activities that they connect with.

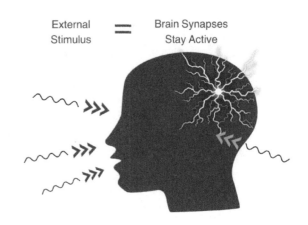

Whether the person physically engages in the activity or not, their brain neurones will still be responding - keeping it active.

The following tips work well with residents who have advanced dementia:

1. Sit down with the resident and casually start doing something that they can watch. No need to get them to participate at this stage.

   Interesting activities might include knitting, potting a plant, plaiting someone's hair, playing with a ball, doing a 3D block puzzle, or simply singing a well-known song.

   If you know what they used to do for a living or hobby, all the better. You could then choose an activity that relates to that to stimulate their interest even more.

   The person might eventually comment on the hairstyle you are creating, or roll the ball back across the table to you. They will find their own way of showing you that they are interested. Test out different activities to see which ones the resident enjoys. Once you see that the resident is engaged, it will feel very rewarding, and the activity itself will be helping to keep their brain active and stimulated.

2. If your resident is in a low mood, they might appreciate simply having their hair brushed, or their hand held for a while. That might be the only interaction they need in that moment.

On the next page is a table of activities you can try out while sitting in front of a resident. You will be able to add your own ideas to the list.

	Activity	Engagement opportunity
1.	Sit at a table with the resident and casually play with a soft ball until they make eye contact.	If they show any interest at all, then roll it across the table to them. They might surprise you and roll it back. Advance to playing throw and catch. People with advanced dementia often still have good hand to eye co-ordination.
2.	Research the hairstyles that the resident might have had in their youth. Recreate those styles in front of them, using ribbons, grips and a comb.	Keep changing the style to engage the observing resident. Ask them what they think of each. If appropriate and safe give them a go with a brush on a mannequin. (Use a table-top hair mannequin, or a willing human!)
3.	Pot a few plants or arrange a bunch of flowers next to a resident who was once a keen gardener.	Give the resident the opportunity to put their hands in the soil, or hand you the flowers. Tell them the names of the plants and flowers as they smell them to boost recall.
4.	Sit with the resident and browse through a book of historical photos from the town where they grew up. If the resident was in the Armed Forces, sit next to them and browse through a book of nostalgic military photos from that era.	Photos or videos of happy places where we grew up is a very powerful way to stimulate brain activity and recall. Discuss the pictures with the resident and read a few interesting facts to them. Let them browse the book if they can. You will find lots of historical 'how we used to live' photo books of varying subjects at your local library or from your local history society.
5.	Sit with the resident and paint a simple picture. Either do this together or let them watch you do it – whichever is appropriate.	If the resident has low capacity but can hold a paint brush, magical colouring pads are great for giving them the sensation of painting. The images appear in colour when brushed with water. This activity is particularly stimulating for those residents who enjoy being creative.
6.	Sit with the resident and start singing a song that they might know the words to.	Try songs of different genres to see what makes them smile or join in. It's important to note that not everyone of a certain era likes Vera Lynn or Frank Sinatra.

7.	Read aloud a short story or poem to the resident. It could be one from their childhood, or an entertaining classic.	The resident's connection with stories, poems and songs will be strong still. Encourage them to join in, and support them if they want to make up their own versions.
8.	Your residents will come from an era of mending household items. As an activity, try mending something simple next to them e.g. fix a simple toy, or darn some socks. ***Important! Follow your care home's health and safety/risk assessment procedures around potentially dangerous objects.**	Watching this activity (or taking part if the senior care team says that it safe for them to do so) will engage most residents. If you have a budget there are 3D block puzzles that you can buy and construct, specially designed for people with dementia. What other objects could you safely 'repair' or 'construct' while a resident watches/offers assistance?

TASK: Identify a resident in your care setting who has dementia, and who could benefit from more mental stimulation. Then do some background research into their previous pastimes, jobs, family holidays etc. List up to 10 things that were of interest to them.

Now think about how you can turn these areas of interest into engaging activities.

List your ideas below then add them to the resident's activity file.

1. ....

2. ....

3. ....

4. ....

5. ....

6. ....

7. ....

8. ....

9. ....

10. ....

SECTION 6

The TOP 10 most successful 'low to zero budget' activities for an elderly care home setting

On the following pages, you will find a TOP 10 list of activities that will keep the elderly residents of a care home engaged. The best part is that none of these activities require a budget or more than one staff member to run. Additionally, each activity is accompanied by the printable resources you need to get you started. We recommend that you add these activities to your weekly schedule.

1. CREATE YOUR OWN STORY

An interactive, high-energy group activity, delivered by the activity coordinator or a professional storyteller.

 BENEFICIAL OUTCOME: A feeling of empowerment for the residents

HOW IT WORKS: Everyone in the room receives a copy of the same vintage photograph – one that shows some sort of people activity. Then the facilitator asks the group to imagine where the scene is taking place, and what the people's names are etc. The questions encourage the residents to shout out funny responses, which you should either memorise or write down to keep building the story. Summarise what has happened in the story so far, before asking the next question.

The responses they give (to place names and animal names etc) will most likely be based on family members, pets, and places etc that are important to them, so never dismiss an answer as being silly. Always try and include it somewhere in the story. An example of how it could go is:

ACTIVITY COORDINATOR: "What shall we say the people's names are?"

RESIDENTS: (shouting out) 'Clive' 'Mavis' etc...

ACTIVITY COORDINATOR: "Where do you think they are?"

RESIDENT 1: SKEGNESS

RESIDENT 2: NORTHAMPTON

ACTIVITY COORDINATOR: "So, Mavis and Clive were sick of sitting at home in their house in Northampton, so they decided that they were going to take a day trip to Skegness! How do you think they got there?"

Have fun keeping the story moving and try to create a happy or fun ending. Be prepared to offer suggestions and guide the story as necessary. Continuously recap on the progress of the story, and at the end read it back to the group. This will not only be a nostalgic experience for the residents, but also a collaborative effort that they can take pride in creating. Use different photos and questions in future sessions.

RESOURCES FOR ACTIVITY 1: Create Your Own Story

Example questions for you to use to facilitate your story and move it forward.

The image to accompany these questions is on the next page. Print the image and give each resident their own copy to refer to.

1. Where should we say this place is?
2. What should we name these two people?
3. Why are they there?
4. How do they know each other?
5. How do they get on?
6. How are they feeling, and why?
7. Who else is with them, that we can't see in the picture?
8. What is he thinking?
9. What is she thinking?
10. What else is happening around them that we can't see?
11. What sounds can they hear? (Get the resident's 'seaside' senses going)
12. What can they smell?
13. Who do you think wears the trousers out of those two?
14. What does he do for a living?
15. What does she do for a living?
16. What does he really think of her?
17. What does she really think of him?
18. Are they good neighbours to those living next door?
19. What did he want to be as a child?
20. What did she want to be as a child?
21. What are they having for their lunch?
22. How does it taste?
23. Do they have a family? Who are they?
24. What do they think of their family?
25. What happens next?
26. How should our story end?

RESOURCE FOR ACTIVITY 1: 'Create Your Own Story' session.

2. SUPER QUIZ + MUSIC

An interactive quiz that all your residents can take part in by shouting out the answers.

 BENEFICIAL OUTCOME: Improved mood and confidence.

HOW IT WORKS:

Host an hour-long general knowledge quiz for the residents. The questions should be varied and cover a wide range of subject areas. Remember that a lot of your residents are well travelled and have had challenging jobs in the past, so don't make all the questions easy.

Top Tip 1: Have a look at the resident's activity files and discover the subjects that they are interested in. Then you can add some questions around those themes, meaning that every resident will be able to answer at least one question.

Top Tip 2: Begin your quiz sessions by playing songs that the residents can sing along to. This will increase the energy level in the room as people are arriving.

RESOURCE FOR ACTIVITY 2: Super Quiz

On the next page you will find a quiz sheet to get you started. The quiz has been specially designed to include questions that take all capacities and interests into consideration.

⇒ You can free up your quiz-making time by buying our Ultimate Quiz Book for Seniors. It has 52 quizzes like the one included on the next page – A year's worth of work, done! Buy it by searching on Amazon, or by scanning this code.

RESOURCE FOR ACTIVITY 2: Super Quiz

	QUESTIONS	ANSWERS
1	WHAT WAS THE NAME OF THE ELEPHANT WHO PACKED HER TRUNK AND SAID GOODBYE TO THE CIRCUS?	NELLIE
2	A TABLESPOON IS HOW MANY TEASPOONS?	THREE
3	ON WHAT TYPE OF SURFACE IS CURLING PLAYED?	ICE
4	COMPLETE THE PROVERB 'A BAD PENNY...'	ALWAYS TURNS UP
5	HOW MANY WIVES DID HENRY VIII HAVE?	SIX
6	CAN YOU NAME THEM?	CATHERINE OF ARAGON, ANNE BOLEYN, JANE SEYMOUR, ANNE OF CLEVES, CATHERINE HOWARD, CATHERINE PARR
7	CAMPANOLOGY IS THE TERM FOR WHICH ACTIVITY?	BELL RINGING
8	IN THE SONG, WHERE DID A NIGHTINGALE SING?	BERKELEY SQUARE
9	WHICH COUNTRY'S NATIONAL ANTHEM IS 'THE STAR-SPANGLED BANNER'?	USA
10	IN THE RHYME, WHAT FRIGHTENED MISS MUFFET?	A SPIDER
11	GIVE 10 BOYS NAMES BEGINNING WITH A	ADRIAN, ANDREW, AARON, ALEX, ALFRED, ARNOLD, ANGUS, ARTHUR, ALVIN, ARCHIE + MORE
12	NAME THE 3 AMERICAN STATES THAT BEGIN WITH C?	CALIFORNIA, CONNECTICUT, AND COLORADO
13	WHICH 1937 FILM FEATURES THE SONG 'WHISTLE WHILE YOU WORK'?	SNOW WHITE AND THE SEVEN DWARVES
14	IN WHICH CLASSIC CHILDREN'S STORY DID A STRANGE LITTLE MAN SPIN STRAW INTO GOLD?	RUMPELSTILTSKIN
15	WHAT IS 7 X 7?	49
16	IN THE FILM, WHAT PROFESSION WAS MR CHIPS?	A TEACHER
17	IN WHICH ENGLISH COUNTY IS CHEDDAR GORGE?	SOMERSET
18	WHERE IN FRANCE WERE THE D-DAY LANDINGS?	NORMANDY
19	WHOSE REPORT IN THE 1960s LED TO THE AXING OF A THIRD OF BRITAIN'S RAILWAY NETWORK?	DR BEECHING
20	WHERE IS THE MATTERHORN?	SWITZERLAND

Printable Resource from The Ultimate Handbook for Activity Coordinators

 # 3. STORYTELLING FOR EVERYONE

Read out a short story or poem that lasts about 10-15 mins.

 BENEFICIAL OUTCOME: Improved mood for your residents and a boost of confidence for the reader.

HOW IT WORKS:

Here is where your talent as an activity coordinator will shine.

Read your residents a story that lasts approximately 10 – 15 minutes.

Ask them about their favourite stories or poems before the session, and then try to find a version online for you to read. They may even have their own copy to lend you.

Browning's Pied Piper of Hamlin is one that many elderly people loved as a child, and they adore hearing it again. In fact, it was Tom, one of my former residents, who taught it to me! Why not give it a go?

If any of your residents prefer to stay in their rooms, you could also read to them / print off a copy for them.

On the next page you will find a nice traditional short story to get you started. You'll find more in the library or online.

THE LEGEND OF THE CEDAR TREE

Cherokee Native American story

A long time ago when the Cherokee People were new to the Earth, they decided that life might be better if night did not exist, so they prayed to Ouga the creator to take away the darkness and leave only the day.

Ouga heard their voices and immediately released Grandmother moon from her work, asking her to take her blanket of dark sky with her. In her place, Grandfather sun appeared, and there he remained from that moment on.

But with the continual sun, the forests grew thick, and the pathways between the villages and homes disappeared beneath the heavy growth of vegetation. The people were forced to work for hours each day, pulling up weeds that were smothering their corn and other food plants. The days became hot and long, and soon the villagers found it impossible to sleep, growing irritable, and quarrelling with their neighbours over the smallest of things. They realised their terrible mistake in asking for a world without night, so they prayed once again to the Creator.

"Ouga," they begged. "We wished for constant daylight, but we were wrong. Please take away the sun and make it constant night instead."

The creator pondered on what was being asked; thinking about how all things were created in twos to keep balance – day and night, life and death, times of plenty and times of famine. But Ouga held great love for the people, and so decided to grant their request.

Grandfather sun was released from his duty, and Grandmother moon returned, casting her dark blanket over the Earth. But the night brought with it a freezing cold air, and the people were now forced to spend all their time gathering wood for the fires to try and stay warm. Without the sun, their crops stopped growing, and it was too dark to hunt, so eventually they became hungry and weak, and many died.

So once more the people turned to the Creator. "Ouga, please help us. We have made another terrible mistake. What you created in the beginning was perfect – as it should be. We ask that you forgive us and make day and night come in turns as before."

The Creator heard their prayers and soon the sun was shining down upon them – only this time it sank below the horizon each evening, allowing night to take its rightful place in the sky. The weather became more pleasant, and within a few days new food crops were poking up from the ground. The people were able to hunt again, and there was no more hunger. As they wanted for nothing, the people returned to treating each other with respect and kindness. They gathered to thank the Creator for the gift of life, and for all that was sacred, and Ouga accepted their gratitude. But still feeing sad for those who had died during the days of darkness, Ouga gathered up their spirits and created a new type of tree, then placed them in it. The new tree was named, a-tsi-na-tlu-gv *(Ah-see-na-loo-guh)* – 'Cedar Tree.'

From then on, whenever the people stood before the cedar tree, they could feel the spirit of their ancestors among them, and as the cedar trees spread through the forest, they carried those spirits with them.

And it is believed to this day that the wood of the great Cedar tree still holds the spirits of our ancestors within its bark, and if you carry a small piece with you at all times, they will protect you. But if you simply choose to stand and gaze upon these mighty friends, have no doubt that they will be gazing down upon you too.

THE END

4. GROUP EXERCISES TO MUSIC

30 minutes of seated exercises. Simple movements that activity coordinators can lead.

 BENEFICIAL OUTCOME: Improved health, mobility, and mood.

HOW IT WORKS:

30 mins of basic physical exercise is required at least twice a week to maintain mobility and health – especially as we get older and our bodies start to lose muscle mass and strength. One of the essential roles of an activity coordinator is to encourage physical movement – even if seated. This can be done as a group, or as 1-1 sessions. Simple movements such as arm raises, seated marching, and swimming motions are effective and fun.

TOP TIP FOR ENCOURAGING RELUCTANT RESIDENTS TO EXERCISE:

1. Avoid asking them whether they want to exercise, as they'll generally say no. Instead, turn on some music that they enjoy, Then, sit down at the front of the room and say something like: **'We're going to do some light exercises. Join in if you want. It's okay if you don't want to.'** Then start on the first exercise, calling out the instructions over the music. You'll find that most of the residents will eventually join in.

2. Advertise the exercise sessions as 'Light Exercises with Frank Sinatra' (Or any other artist they like). They are more likely to attend if they know that there is some good music playing. Then do the exercises while Frank is playing in the background. Inject some fun by all singing along.

On the next page, you will find a list of exercises appropriate for elderly people. Please check with your senior carers or manager before you start.

Royal Devon and Exeter
NHS Foundation Trust

Seated Exercise Programme

Exercise 1

With feet flat on the floor, tap toes and lift heels alternately.

Repeat 20 times on each foot

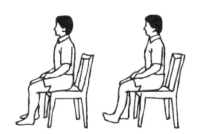

Exercise 2

Pull your toes up, tighten your thigh muscle and straighten your knee. Hold for approximately 5 seconds and then slowly relax your leg.

Repeat 20 times on each leg

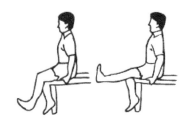

Exercise 3

Sit tall with your arms at your sides. Lift both shoulders up to your ears, draw them back, then press them down.

Repeat the circle 20 times

Exercise 4

Marching feet on the spot, lifting knees up and down.

Repeat 20 times on each foot

Exercise 5

Lift each leg up and out to the side, then back to the middle. Repeat with other leg.

Repeat 20 times on each leg

(Version date: July 2020)

63

Exercise 6

Place your right hand on your left knee, then turn your upper body and head towards your left arm. Repeat on the opposite side.

Repeat 10 times on each side

Exercise 7

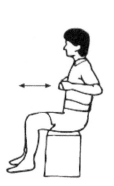

Sit away from the chair back. Bend your elbows and swing your arms from the shoulder.
Build to a rhythm that is comfortable for you.

Repeat 20 times

Exercise 8

Alternate lifting your arms from your chest straight up and bring back down.

Repeat 20 times on each arm

Exercise 9

Reach your arms forward, straightening your elbow, then bring your arms back, bending your elbows and bringing them into your sides, in a 'rowing' action.

Repeat 20 times

Exercise 10

Hold the arms of the chair and attempt to lift your bottom from the seat by straightening your arms and pushing your shoulders down.

Repeat 20 times

Exercise 11

Practice pushing up into a semi-standing position.

Repeat 20 times

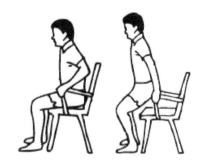

5. BINGO with PRIZES

A fun game of bingo with simple prizes to give away.

☑ **BENEFICIAL OUTCOME: Improved mood.**

HOW IT WORKS:

Simply, get the bingo cards out and have fun.

You can buy a bingo ball machine online for less than £10. Or you can create your own with ping-pong balls /screwed up paper, which you then number 1 to 90 and pick out of a bag or bowl. You can buy large bingo cards or make your own.

Making the cards yourself gives you the option to make A4 sized bingo cards for those who have visual impairments. If you create approximately 20 different cards as master copies, you can just photocopy them for each new game. Just make sure that no two people in the room get the same card during the same game.

THE RULES OF BINGO: In case you're not familiar with the rules of bingo, everyone gets their own individual card with a different set of numbers on each. The host then picks balls at random from the machine/bag and calls out the number, which the players cross off if it appears on their card. Make sure that each ball that is pulled goes into a separate place – not back in the bag.

Keep the game going for longer by first getting them to complete a line. The first person to cross off an entire horizontal line shouts, 'BINGO.' The numbers on their card are checked against the ones that have been pulled out, and if they match, they get a prize. Then the game continues (keeping the same cards) until all of the numbers on someone's card are crossed off. This is called a 'full house.' The first person to get a full house shouts out, and if their numbers match when checked, they win, and the game is over.

Give out biscuit/crisp prizes to the winners (place them on a stand so that they get to choose their prize).

BINGO CARDS!

Here are twelve bingo game card templates to get you started. Each game is 9 x 3 squares. The units 1-9 are in the first column, the tens are in the second column, the twenties in the third column, and so on. The number 90 can go in the same column as the 80s. This is the traditional set up that your residents will be used to, and it will make it easier for them to find the numbers.

BINGO (left card)

	12		38		58		73	85
		24		49	51	69		87
5			37	48		64	74	
2	15		34	46			75	
		25		44		60	71	80
				47	57	61	70	88
		23	32		54	65	78	
4	17	28			59		79	
	13		36	41		66		82
8	11	20			56		76	
9	18	29	33	43				
3		22		40		62		83
1	16	21		42		68		
			35		53	63	77	81
	14	27	39		55			90
6	10	26	31					84
7					50	67	72	89
	19		30	45	52			86

BINGO (right card)

		29		45	53		70	84
8	15	25		46			77	
5	14		30			63		89
3			32	48			74	81
		28	36	41		67		80
	18	22		42	58			85
		27	38		50	60		86
	13		39	43		65	75	
2	11	23			51	64		
	19		35	49		62		90
7		21		44	55		76	
			34		59	61	72	82
1				47		68	71	87
9	17		33		54		78	
6		26			52	69	79	
	12	24	31		57			88
4	10			40	56			83
	16	20	37			66	73	

And, of course, the residents will expect to hear the traditional bingo calls as each number is drawn. They will know most of them and most likely join in. Feel free to change any that you find outdated or inappropriate now. You can photocopy this page and keep it with your bingo set.

TRADITIONAL BINGO CALLS

1 – Kelly's Eye	24 – two dozen	47 – four and seven	70 – three score and ten
2 – one little duck	25 – duck and dive	48 – four dozen	71 – bang on the drum
3 – cup of tea	26 – pick and mix	49 - PC	72 – six dozen
4 – knock at the door	27 – gateway to heaven	50 – half a century	73 – queen bee
5 - man alive	28 – in a state	51 – tweak of the thumb	74 – hit the floor
6 – Tom mix/ half a dozen	29 – rise and shine	52 – Danny La Rue	75 – strive and strive
7 – lucky seven	30 – Dirty Gertie	53 – Stuck in a tree	76 - trombones
8 – garden gate	31 – get up and run	54 – clean the floor	77 – Sunset Strip
9 - doctor's orders	32 – buckle my shoe	55 – snakes alive	78 – 39 extra steps
10 – Prime Minister's den	33 – fish, chips and peas	56 – Shotts Bus	79 – one more time
11 – legs eleven	34 – ask for more	57 – Heinz Varieties	80 – eight and blank
12 – one dozen	35 – jump and jive	58 – make them wait	81 – stop and run
13 – unlucky for some	36 – three dozen	59 – Brighton Line	82 – straight on through
14 – Valentine's Day	37 – more than eleven	60 – five dozen	83 – time for tea
15 – young and keen	38 – Christmas cake	61 – baker's bun	84 – seven dozen
16 – sweet sixteen	39 – 39 steps	62 – tickety boo	85 – staying alive
17 - dancing queen	40 – life begins	63 – tickle me 63	86 – between the sticks
18 – coming of age	41 – time for fun	64 – red raw	87 – Torquay in Devon
19 – goodbye teens	42 – Winnie the Pooh	65 – old age pension	88 – two fat ladies
20 – one score	43 – down on your knees	66 – clickety click	89 – nearly there
21 - key of the door	44 – droopy draws	67 – stairway to heaven	90 – top of the shop
22 – two little ducks	45 – halfway there	68 – saving grace	
23 – thee and me	46 – up to tricks	69 – favourite of mine	

6. THE HISTORY OF OUR TOWN

A short talk about the history of a village, town or city

 BENEFICIAL OUTCOME: Improved mood for your residents | Mental recall exercise | Stimulates group conversation | Sense of belonging

HOW IT WORKS:

This activity is a favourite among elderly care home residents. First, research a few interesting facts about the history of the town or place where the home is located and give an enthusiastic history lesson, including some fascinating medieval history e.g. kings or queens that visited, or battles that took place.

More importantly, include facts about landmarks from the 1940s and 50s that they may have visited. This will start some lovely conversations and the residents will enjoy sharing their own memories. Encourage everyone to join in but try not to let the conversation drift off subject. Keep bringing them back to the place or thing you're talking about and teach them something new.

Learn a couple of key dates and significant events associated with the town or place, and then create cards with prompts for yourself so that you don't have to read from a sheet of paper for the entire time.

To gather information, you can use online resources, local history books, archives, and museums. Once you have your prompts ready, you can deliver your history lesson with enthusiasm, inviting the residents to share their own memories and stories.

TOP TIP: Use the facts that you have learned, and the memories that are being shared, to create a lovely, interesting article for your weekly/monthly internal newspaper.

7. THE SECRET STORY OF NURSERY RHYMES

The real history behind the nursery rhymes that we grew up with

 BENEFICIAL OUTCOME: Increased knowledge | Improved mental recall | Stimulation of group conversation | Enjoyable memories and nostalgia

HOW IT WORKS:

Your residents will probably know most of the well-loved nursery rhymes. In fact they will have been reciting them since they were children. Because of this, nursery rhymes are seen as childish, and for entertaining small children, however, what most people don't know is that the traditional nursery rhymes were written in medieval times, and that they have horrible, gruesome, histories behind them.

Your residents will be fascinated to hear that nursery rhymes were never meant for children e.g. that Ring a Ring O' Roses was written about the plague, and that Mary, Mary Quite Contrary is really about the murderous 'Bloody Mary' - the daughter of Henry VIII.

On the following page we have provided you with the histories of three well-known nursery rhymes to get you started, but for future activity sessions, have a look at the history of the following nursery rhymes and create another interesting and entertaining, 'The Secret Story of Nursery Rhymes' talk.

Future ideas:

- Humpty Dumpty was really a siege cannon used in the English Civil War in 1648.

- Jack and Jill. There are lots of theories behind the history of Jack and Jill, but one is that Jack and Jill were really King Louis XVI of France, and Queen Marie Antoinette who were both beheaded.

There are lots more hidden histories of nursery rhymes to be found!

The REAL horrible history behind our well known nursery rhymes

Did you know that most of our nursery rhymes were made up by the downtrodden people as sarcastic commentary on what was happening politically in the country? They were not for children at all. Whenever you recite a nursery rhyme you are engaging with a centuries old tradition of historical storytelling.

Here are the interesting stories behind some of our well known rhymes.

Ring a Ring o Roses

Ring a Ring o Roses is widely believed to be about the 1665 Great Plague of London. The roses, or "rosie" is the blotchy ring of red rash that developed on the face of bubonic plague sufferers. During the epidemic, the smell of the disease was so bad that people would carry posies of flowers under their noses to hide it. The bubonic plague killed 15% of Britain's population, and so the words "atishoo, atishoo, we all fall down" refers to the plague victims becoming sick and falling down dead.

Mary Mary Quite Contrary

Mary, Mary Quite Contrary is thought to be about Bloody Mary - the daughter of King Henry VIII and Catherine of Aragon. Queen Mary was a staunch Catholic and would torture and killed Protestants who would not convert to Catholicism. The 'garden' that is mentioned in the rhyme refers to the graveyards that were being filled with Protestant Martyrs, while the 'silver bells' and 'cockle shells' were instruments of torture. The 'Pretty maids' were the people who were being lined up to await their gruesome fate.

Baa Baa Black Sheep

Baa Baa Black Sheep is believed to be about the Great Custom tax on wool that was introduced in the 13th century. The Great Custom tax meant that in the year 1275, sheep farmers now had to split the profits for each bag of wool they sold with the king. So, now the profits on each bag were split between the farmer, the king, and the church. 'None for the little boy who cries down the lane' suggests that the poor shepherd boys were left with no wages due to this heavy tax.

8. YOUR LIFE STORY

An activity session where the residents share memories based around 'The subject of the day.'

 BENEFICIAL OUTCOME: Improved memory and recall | Empowerment | Improved mood | Connection to who they are | Conversation stimulation

HOW IT WORKS:

This is a more empowering activity than purely reminiscing. You can do this in large groups or small.

Depending on the capacity of the residents, start off by asking each resident what their earliest memory is, or what they did for a living, or what pets they had, etc. You could record this information and, with permission, later write it up to make 'memory' booklets that can be shared with other residents in the home, or with their families.

If a resident has full capacity, you could ask them if they would like to arrange a one-to-one session with you, so that you can help them write their life story. To do this, use a recording device to record the conversation, and then write up the notes later. Note: Transcribing audio takes longer than you imagine, so keep the conversations short.

For residents with advanced dementia, photos of industrial environments in which they worked, or household objects, may start a conversation about what they remember. It will certainly stimulate their brain activity.

This activity session will fly by as the residents will enjoy sharing memories. Some of them might discover that they worked in the same place or went to the same school.

Here is a list of questions that you can use to stimulate conversation. You could cover a different subject each week.

1. Where did you grow up? What are your earliest memories?

2. What was your favourite toy as a child? How did you spend your days?

3. What was your school life like? Do you remember who your favourite teacher was, and what subjects you liked? Did you ever get into trouble at school?

4. Tell me about your birthdays. What did you do to celebrate? What presents did you get? How was Christmas day spent? How did you spend the day?

5. What was your house like? Can you describe your living room and kitchen? What was your bedroom like? Did you have any pets? What were their names?

6. Who were your childhood friends? Where did you used to go to play?

7. What did your parents do for a living? What were they like at home? Did you get on with them?

8. Where did you used to go on holiday? Who did you go with? What did you do there?

9. What was your first job? Where was it? Who were your workmates? What transport did you use to get there?

10. How did you spend your evenings when you were a teenager? Do you remember your first love?

11. What hobbies have you had in your life? Where did you do them? What memories do you have of them?

12. What fashions were 'in' when you were a teenager/in your twenties? Do you have any fond memories of the shopkeepers?

9. SING-ALONG WITH TEA AND CAKES

A simple sing-along with sweet refreshments

 BENEFICIAL OUTCOME: Improved mood | Social interaction | memory stimulation

HOW IT WORKS:

The week before the activity session, ask each of the residents which singers/musicians that they like, and then make a compilation playlist of these sing-along tunes to play during the session. The residents will either sing along or just enjoy listening to their favourite tunes.

If you want, you can print out the words to one or two of the classics – however, this is very time consuming so you might want to start with one or two lyric sheets to begin with and build up the song sheets over time. Keep the sheets in a file and photocopy them as needed.

Make sure that each of the residents' choices are played if possible. If not in one session, then definitely during the next one. Then get your pinny on and serve them tea and cakes from a stand while you're all singing.

Some song suggestions that they will all know:

1) Daisy Daisy
2) Bless 'Em All (The Long and the Short and the Tall)
3) You Are My Sunshine
4) We'll Meet Again
5) It's A Long Way to Tipperary
6) Underneath The Arches
7) It's a Sin to Tell a Lie
8) Singin' In the Rain
9) Pack up Your Troubles in Your Old Kit Bag
10) New York, New York **(Tip! A good song to end on)**

10. FILM AFTERNOON WITH CINEMA SWEETS

Put on a classic film in the lounge, and up serve tea and cake

 **BENEFICIAL OUTCOME: Improved mood | Company | Relaxation**

HOW IT WORKS:

Ask the residents what their favourite film is, then choose one each week to put on in the group lounge /film room, while you serve them traditional sweets and cinema snacks. Simple!

This is a great opportunity for you to go off and do your planning/paperwork or carry out some 1-1 sessions with other residents.

Some popular film ideas as a back-up:

1) Calamity Jane
2) South Pacific
3) Ladies in Lavender
4) The Lady in the Van
5) The King's Speech
6) On Golden Pond
7) Billy Elliot
8) Some Like it Hot
9) Planes, Trains and Automobiles
10) Anne of Green Gables

Some Christmas favourites
11) Downton Abbey
12) My Fair Lady
13) Mary Poppins
14) The Wizard of Oz
15) By The Light of the Silvery Moon

Free Resources – where to find them

For the activity coordinators who have zero budget, here is a list of useful free resources. Follow the website URL, or scan the QR code, which will take you straight to the page.

*The following resources were available at the time of this book being published.

NESTLÉ

Nestlé has a fantastic, downloadable Reminiscence Pack on their website. You can print off vintage labels for tins and chocolate bars, and build your own vintage boxes. You can also print off archive posters and old board games for free. **Top Tip:** You could create nostalgic centrepieces for the dining room tables to stimulate conversation. Or wrap modern sweets in the old packaging during a film afternoon.
https://www.nestle.co.uk/en-gb/aboutus/reminiscencepack

YOUTUBE

YouTube is a great place to find free historical videos of your local area – or the area of interest to the residents. You will also find old films and TV programmes that the residents would have watched – including old children's programmes, which are always popular! There are vintage radio shows, documentaries, concerts, and 'how to make' tutorials too. Just do a search for a particular subject and see what comes up. If you have a smart TV, you can find YouTube on that, otherwise you might need to stream/plug a phone or tablet into the TV.
https://www.youtube.com

GOOGLE MAPS

Google Maps is fantastic for taking a walk down memory lane. If you ask a resident which street they grew up on, then type that into the Google Maps search bar, it will take you to an aerial view of that street. Once you have located the right place, look for a little yellow figure at the bottom right of the screen. Drag that figure onto the street and you will be able to virtually walk along it using the arrows, to show the resident how it looks today. You might even be able to find their old house. But you don't have to stop there. You could have a look around any place in the world. Why not take a stroll along Hollywood Boulevard? Or have a look around the streets of Sydney?
https://www.google.com/maps

NATIONAL ACTIVITY PROVIDERS ASSOCIATION (NAPA)

NAPA has lots of free activity resources and ideas for you to use. It is also a useful site to find support in your role as an activity coordinator. Below is a link to their free resources page but have a look around their entire website to find more free resources.
https://napa-activities.co.uk/services/resources/free-resources

There are several businesses that sell digital subscriptions to elderly care home activity resources. If you have a budget, you will be able to find them with a simple website search.

BONUS IDEA: CREATE YOUR OWN SEASONAL NEWSPAPER OR NEWSLETTER

If you have the time, you could use some of the resources to create your internal, seasonal newspaper. Give it a title such as, 'The Past Times.'

It could feature:

1. A particular resident's memories of a subject – gathered from the Life Story group sessions.
2. Puzzles such as 'spot the difference,' or 'crosswords.'
3. An article on this season's flowers and wildlife.
4. Celebrity biographies of well-known film stars/singers from the residents' younger days.
5. An *'On This Date in History,'* section that discusses historical events of note.
6. Photographs of the care home's recent trips out, special events, or visiting entertainers.
7. A 'postcard' featuring different cities, and facts of interest.

It could include whatever you want. Maybe some of your residents would like to write an article, short story, or poem to be included? Be creative and have fun!

A great resource for free newspaper/newsletter templates is CANVA **www.Canva.com** It also gives you free images and interesting texts to use.

So, all that's left to say is, good luck!
We hope that you found this handbook useful and that you are inspired to create an awesome timetable of activities for your residential care home!

You can also join our free Facebook community group and watch free video tutorials on everything in this book. Search for 'Free Care Home Activities Coaching.'

We look forward to seeing you there!

We'd love to hear how you get on. If you have found this book useful, please leave us a nice review on the platform that you bought it from! We're a tiny business and reviews really help us to become visible to more activity coordinators. Thank you.

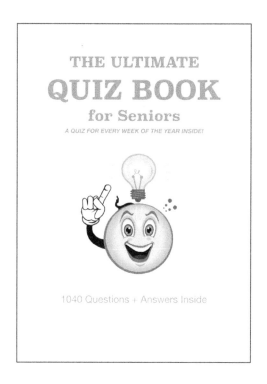

Other resources from Successful Care Home Activities:

The Ultimate Quiz Book for Seniors

A quiz book based on the memories, current affairs knowledge, and interests of people aged 65+

Available from Amazon books!

Printed in Great Britain
by Amazon

Printed in Great Britain
by Amazon

46453515R00044